Cockroach

DAVID ORME

Ransom

Cockroach
by David Orme
Illustrated by Jorge Mongiovi and Ulises Carpintero
Cover photograph: © Marcus Jones

Published by Ransom Publishing Ltd.
Radley House, 8 St. Cross Road, Winchester, Hampshire SO23 9HX
www.ransom.co.uk

ISBN   978 184167 452 0

First published in 2011

Printed and bound in India by Nutech Print Services

CONTENTS

THE RUBBISH PILE

City View Flats were in West Road. Seb Brown was the caretaker. He mended anything that was broken, and dealt with the rubbish. The people who lived in the flats brought their rubbish downstairs in black sacks. Seb took the sacks out each week, and the bin men took them away.

Seb was cross. The bin men were on strike, and the rubbish was beginning to pile up in the yard at the back of the flats. If it got any

worse, people wouldn't be able to park their cars there.

Seb took another rubbish sack out. He threw it on top of the other sacks. Phew – what a terrible smell!

He looked to see where the smell was coming from. One of the sacks was ripped open. The local cats must have done it. They knew that the sacks were full of meat bones and other food.

'I'll get another sack,' thought Seb. He went to his store and found one. He would put the torn sack inside it. He lifted up the torn sack – and the smell got worse!

Under the sack was the body of a cat. There wasn't much left of it. The bones seemed to have been picked clean. The fur and skin was left. This was rotting in the hot sun.

Just then, Seb felt something crawling up his sleeve. He dropped the sack with a yell.

He felt a pain. It was like being stabbed. He tore off his shirt. A huge cockroach was fixed to his arm. He pulled at it, and it fell to the ground. He stamped on it. Even though it was crushed, the cockroach's feelers carried on moving.

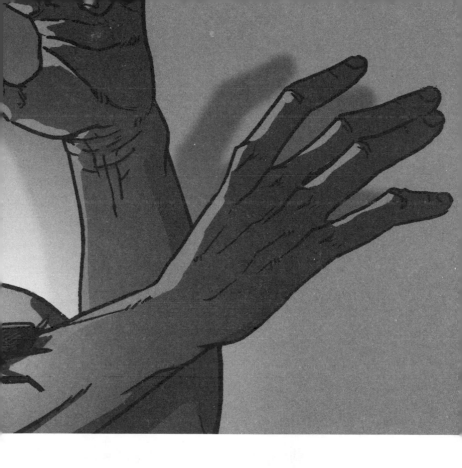

Seb heard a rustling sound behind him. He looked at the sack he had dropped. More huge cockroaches were pouring out of it, running over his feet, trying to climb up his legs ...

2

WHERE ARE THEY?

It could have been worse for Seb. He managed to get the cockroaches off his legs before he was bitten too badly. Mrs Rickard from the flats took him to hospital.

'You need an injection,' she said. 'Those bites could turn nasty.'

When Seb got back from the hospital, he rang the council. He wanted someone to come and deal with the pests.

'I'm sorry,' said the voice on the phone. 'The pest officer is busy. There is rubbish everywhere. He is busy dealing with rats.'

Then Seb had an idea. Dr Phillips! He lived in a flat at the top of the building. He was a biologist – he worked at the university, studying living things.

It was Saturday, and Dr Phillips was at home. Seb explained what had happened.

'I don't think they can be cockroaches,' said Dr Phillips. 'Cockroaches don't attack people!'

He came down the backyard with Seb. They couldn't find any cockroaches. Dr Phillips looked at the one Seb had crushed.

'It does look a bit like a cockroach,' said Dr Phillips. 'But it's too squashed to tell. What a stink! The whole area needs spraying with disinfectant.'

Seb had plenty of disinfectant. He went to his cupboard in the basement to get it.

When he got there, he found where the
cockroaches had got to.

NOT FOR THE PUBLIC TO KNOW
TOP SECRET
ZONE 13 FILES ONLY

IN THE BASEMENT

As soon as Seb opened the door he heard them. The basement area was crawling with cockroaches. They seemed to be able to hear him. Hundreds of them turned towards the door.

Seb slammed the door just in time. Some of the cockroaches had already reached it. They were crushed as the door slammed shut.

He rushed to fetch Dr Phillips again.

'The basement is full of them!'

Dr Phillips didn't really believe that the cockroaches were dangerous. He thought Seb was making it up. He came down to the basement.

'Mind out of the way!' he said. He threw open the door.

The cockroaches poured out. Within seconds, Dr Phillips was covered with them. He went down screaming. He tried to pull the insects away from his face.

There was nothing Seb could do. He knew that if he stayed there, the cockroaches would get him too. He rushed upstairs to phone the police.

EVERYBODY OUT!

The building would be full of cockroaches in minutes. Seb hit the fire alarm button. That would get everyone out.

People started coming down the stairs.

'Hurry up! Get outside the building!'

Nobody was pleased.

'Where's the fire then?' they grumbled. 'We can't smell smoke!'

Just then, the police arrived. They thought Seb was mad at first. One of the police

officers went to the top of the basement steps.
The cockroaches had reached the top!

The policeman jumped back with a yell.
Cockroaches were crawling up his leg. The
other police officers managed to beat them
off.

'Everyone outside!' yelled a policewoman.
The door to the building was firmly shut.

'Is everyone out?' asked one of the officers.

The people who lived in the flats looked around.

'Where's Mrs James?' someone said.

Seb suddenly remembered. Mrs James was deaf! She couldn't hear the fire alarm! She was still in her flat – with her young baby!

Seb looked at the police officers.

'We've got to get her out!' he said.

THE RESCUE

'The fire brigade will be here soon. They will have special clothing,' said one of the officers.

'We can't wait that long. If you won't do it, I will!' said Seb.

One of the police officers said he would help. He went back into the building with Seb. They started up the stairs. Seb was careful to shut the fire-doors behind him.

Mrs James lived on the third floor. Seb and the policeman soon reached the door to her flat. She could not hear the doorbell. The policeman kicked the door down.

The door led into a little hall.

It was full of cockroaches!

A coat was hanging by the door. The policeman took it. He shook off the cockroaches and put the coat over his head. He charged along the hall. The cockroaches rushed towards him. Some of them dropped on him from the ceiling, but he was too quick for them.

Some of the cockroaches turned towards Seb. He started jumping on them. He heard them crunch under his feet. They kept on coming.

The policeman came back. He had Mrs James with him – and the baby! The baby was wrapped in a blanket. It was quite safe.

Mrs James had been trapped in her kitchen. The cockroaches had just started crawling under the door to reach her. She had cockroaches in her hair. Seb and the policeman managed to pull them out. Their hands were badly bitten.

'They must have travelled up through the heating system,' said Seb. 'They knew exactly where the people were.'

THE END OF THE COCKROACHES?

Soon the fire brigade arrived. They sealed the building. Insect scientists came to look at the cockroaches.

'They are a new species,' they said. 'We've never seen anything like them before.'

They used strong insect killer to try and wipe out the cockroaches. It didn't have any effect on them. The next day the building was still sealed up. It was too dangerous to go in.

'I just don't know what to try next,' said the chief scientist.

Just then, there was a huge explosion. People outside the building ran for their lives. The building started to collapse. Flames leapt up through the rubble.

Seb guessed what had happened. The cockroaches must have got into the big gas boiler. They had caused a gas leak!

The fire brigade started to put out the fire, but the chief scientist stopped them.

'Let it burn!' he said. 'The fire will destroy them.'

Days later, Seb came back to the flats. There was nothing left but bricks and rubble. He couldn't see a single cockroach.

Seb couldn't see the cockroach eggs, either. They were too small.

Inside each egg, a tiny cockroach was growing.

ABOUT THE AUTHOR

David Orme is an expert on strange, unexplained events. For his protection (and yours) we cannot show a photograph of him.

David created the Zone 13 files to record the cases he studied. Some of these files really do involve aliens, but many do not. Aliens are not everywhere. Just in most places.

These stories are all taken from the Zone 13 files. They will not be here for long. Read them while you can.

But don't close your eyes when you go to sleep at night. **They** will be watching you.